Gg **Hh** **Ii** **Jj** **Kk** **Ll** **Mm**

Uu **Vv** **Ww** **Xx** **Yy** **Zz**

Dear Parent,

The My First Steps to Reading® *series is based on a teaching activity that helps children learn to recognize letters and their sounds. The use of predictable language patterns and repetition of familiar words will also help your child build a basic sight vocabulary. Your child will enjoy watching the characters in the books place imaginative objects in "letter boxes." You and your child can even create and fill your own letter box, using stuffed animals, cut-out pictures, or other objects beginning with the same letter. The things you can do together are limited only by your imagination. Learning letters will be fun—the first important step on the road to reading.*

The Editors

My "s" Book

(Blends are included in this book.)

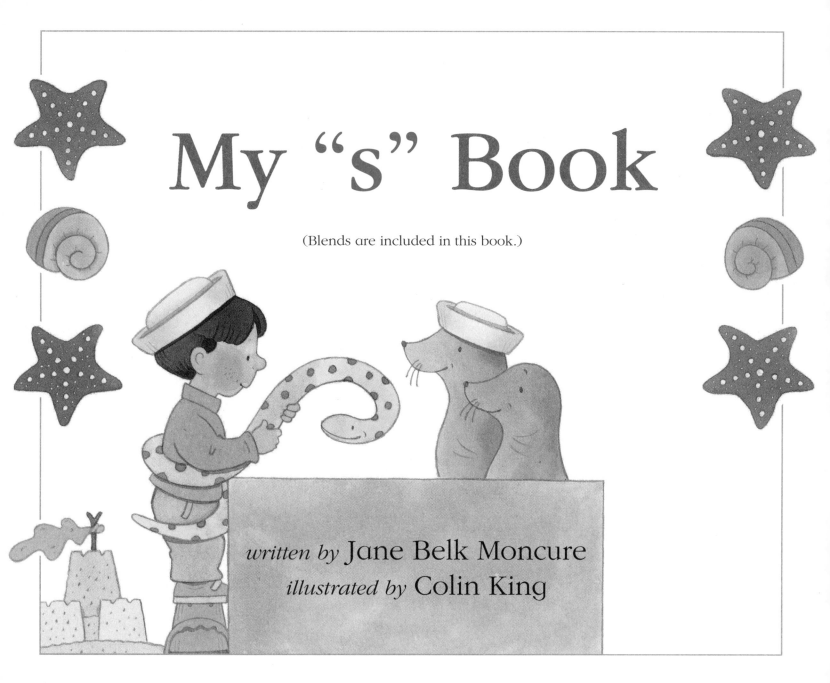

written by Jane Belk Moncure

illustrated by Colin King

Little  S had a box.

"I will find things that begin
with my 's' sound," he said.

"I will put them into
my sound  box."

Little  took off his sneakers,

his socks,

and his sweatshirt.

Did he put the sneakers, socks, and sweatshirt into his box? He did.

Then Little  went for a swim in the sea.

Little S put on his sandals and went for a walk on the sand.

He found a spade  and a
sand bucket.

He made a sand castle.

Then he put the spade,
the sand bucket, and
the sand castle into his  box.

Then Little **S** saw a seal swimming in the sea.

He saw six more seals on the sand.
Did he put the seven seals into his box?

He did.

Little **S** found seashells all over the sand.

He also found a  starfish.

Did he put the seashells
and the starfish into his box?

He did.

Then Little  saw a sea snake.

It was a small sea snake.

He slipped it into a sack.

Then he put the
sack with the sea
snake into the box.

Later, Little  met a sailor.

The sailor gave him a

 sailor hat.

"Let's play," said the sailor.

They played on the

seesaw.

They slid down the slide.

21

Then they swung on the swings.

Suddenly, there was a big, noisy sound!

The sound was coming from the box.

"What is in the box?" asked the sailor.

"Things that begin with my 's' sound," said Little S.

"I sail on things that begin with your sound," said the sailor. "I sail on a

steam ship."

"And I sail in a submarine."

The sailor helped Little 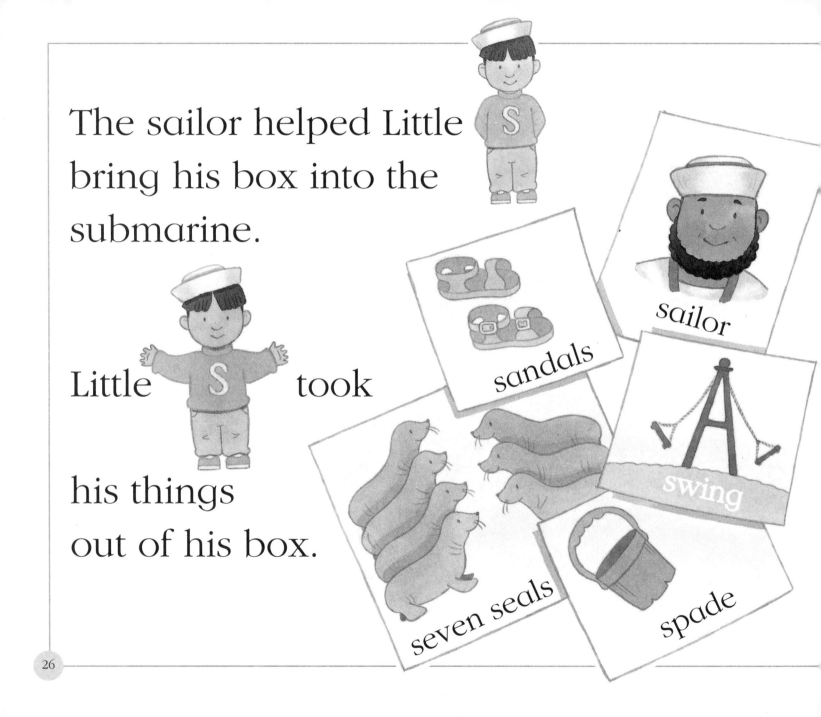 bring his box into the submarine.

Little took his things out of his box.

sandals

sailor

swing

seven seals

spade

The sailor drew pictures of them and of himself. He also drew the swing, the slide, and the seesaw.

sack

slide

starfish

sailor hat

seesaw

seashells

sweatshirt

sand castle

socks

sea snake

Can you read these words with Little 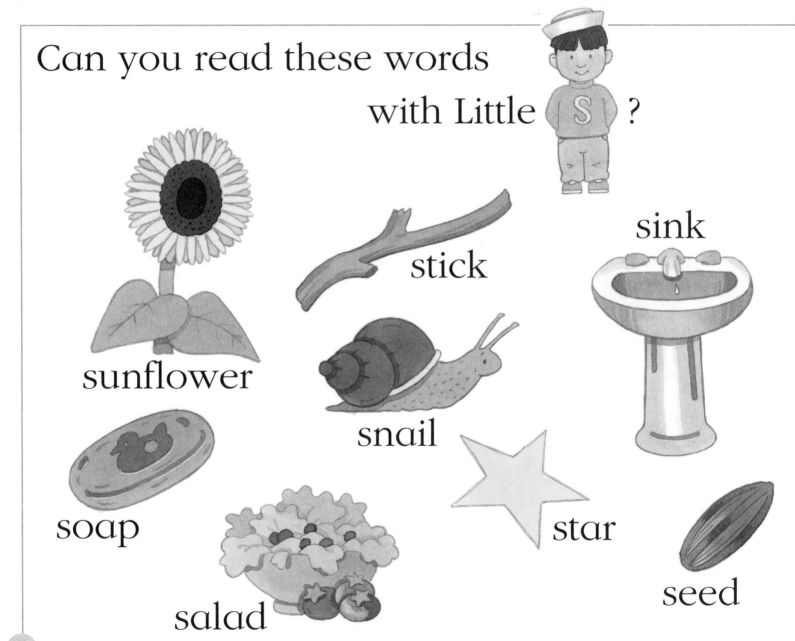 ?

sunflower

stick

sink

snail

soap

salad

star

seed

28

saw

soup

square

sun

stool

stone

stamp

Aa Bb Cc Dd Ee Ff

Nn Oo Pp Qq Rr Ss Tt

My First
Steps to
READING®